Voices From The Belvidere

MONOLOGUES FROM A FEVER HOSPITAL

First Published in 2017
By Glasgow Women's Library
23 Landressy Street
Glasgow G40 1BP

**GLASGOW
WOMEN'S
LIBRARY**

Safeguarding the history of your grandmothers.
Hearing the memories of your mothers.
Providing the inspiration for your daughters.

Supported by
The National Lottery®
through the Heritage Lottery Fund

Le taic bhon
Chrannchur Nàiseanta
tro Mhaoin-Dualchais a' Chrannchuir

ISBN - 978-0-9522273-8-0

Image: NHS Greater Glasgow & Clyde Archives
Photo credits: Glasgow Women's Library and
NHS Greater Glasgow & Clyde Archives
Designed by Rachele Dunn
Printed by J Thomson, Carnoustie Place, Glasgow G5 8PB

Contents

Contents

Voices From The Belvidere

Introduction

When Alice Mackenzie, a woman with local connections, came into Glasgow Women's Library to donate her memoir and a collection of family photographs and other memorabilia, we were intrigued to discover that her mother, Alice Brown (nee Bauchop), had worked at the Belvidere Fever Hospital, just along the road from our home in Glasgow's East End. We knew that we wanted to do something with this serendipitous connection. Thanks to generous funding from the Heritage Lottery Fund's First World War: Then and Now programme, we were able to develop our Voices From The Belvidere project.

We wanted to explore and tell the stories of women who had a connection with the Hospital, now demolished but formerly a building known to so many on London Road in Parkhead – whether as patients, nurses, doctors, maids, visitors – during and around the period of World War I.

Glasgow was an overcrowded and unhealthy place during the 1800s, particularly if you were poor. Industrialisation meant that the city was rapidly expanding and, in the squalid conditions in which the urban poor lived, epidemics of infectious diseases were an ever-present danger.

In 1870, Glasgow experienced a severe epidemic of relapsing fever (a disease borne by lice, causing fever, sickness, chills and aches) and all the available fever beds in the city were quickly filled. The authorities decided that a permanent fever hospital was needed for Glasgow. Belvidere House originally belonged to a tobacco merchant and the house and its thirty-three acre estate were sold to the City in October 1870. Pavilions were hastily built and, by March 1871, these housed 366 patients (although the bed capacity was only 250!). During the three years of the epidemic, over

3,000 cases were treated at the hospital.

Over the next two decades, Belvidere Hospital was expanded and developed. It became the largest of its kind outside London and was full of innovatory features, such as rounded window sills to prevent dust collection. In addition, the Hospital had a large nurses' home where each nurse had her own room – a very attractive proposition for "respectable" young women. The nursing school at Belvidere had an excellent reputation and attracted nurses from all over the UK and Ireland.

The Hospital cared for patients with illnesses such as typhoid, scarlet fever, smallpox, whooping cough, measles, TB, puerperal fever and diphtheria. In 1900 it even housed patients suffering from the bubonic plague after an outbreak in the Gorbals.

Work in a fever hospital was dangerous and tiring; a number of Belvidere nurses and other staff died from diseases acquired from patients, and the records show that a large number of non-nursing staff simply "ran away" or left after refusing to get vaccinated.

The Belvidere remained primarily an infectious diseases hospital until after the formation of the NHS in 1948. It then had a varied life with some of its buildings being used as a maternity unit, a radiotherapy centre and an orthopaedic unit, amongst other things. It later became a general geriatric hospital and care home before closing for good in 1999 and was eventually demolished to make way for housing.

When we were starting the planning for Voices From The Belvidere we sounded out women who came into Glasgow Women's Library. It was fascinating how many of them had connections with the Hospital themselves: as patients, staff, or visitors, or who had mothers or grandmothers who were there, and who told us their stories. We decided that we wanted to uncover and spotlight more of the hidden histories of women associated with this landmark institution.

As so many of the stories of women were missing, partial or vague we decided to create new works, fired by the records, that would mix fact and fiction in an entertaining way and create a dramatic performance piece to celebrate the lives of the women we discovered and shed light on this piece of women's history that was at risk of being lost.

The women involved in the project looked through the archives here at Glasgow Women's Library and also the NHS Greater Glasgow and Clyde Archives at the Mitchell Library. The records are a fascinating and frustrating snapshot of women's lives: fascinating because of the poignant details we discovered, frustrating because we wanted to know so much more.

However, the lack of concrete facts gave participants free rein to be creative. The women used what they found as inspiration to write monologues imagining something of life at the Belvidere: photos of nameless nurses posing formally in their pristine uniforms, playing tennis or having a picnic in the grounds; lists of names and cryptic comments on laundry maids and kitchen staff; indecipherable notes of symptoms and signs of illness in patients; annual reports giving the cold, hard facts of how many cases, how many days spent in hospital, how many deaths.

The result is these wonderful, touching, funny, moving monologues bringing to life the Voices From The Belvidere.

Donna Moore and Nicola Maksymuik,
Glasgow Women's Library

With thanks to Rachele Dunn, Designer-In-Residence at Glasgow Women's Library; Dorothy Sichi, Hannah Wright and all staff and volunteers at GWL; Kirsten Donaldson Wheal, Andrew Gilbert and Alistair Tough of the NHS Greater Glasgow and Clyde Archives at the Mitchell Library; Alice Mackenzie; and the Heritage Lottery Fund.

Special thanks to the women who have so enthusiastically researched, written, rehearsed and performed: Gail Addis, Emma Baker, Suzanne Blackwood, Katy Bullock, Linda Chadha, Louisina Currie, Margaret Daly, Annette Duffy, Margaret Duffy, Georgi Gill, Jo Gray, Kerry Ann Hindley, Oonagh Lawson, Anabel Marsh, Yvonne McFadden, Lyn McLaughlin, Mary Alice McLellan, Kate McNab, Tracy McPherson, Rachel Meach, Gillian Mellor, Kathryn Munro, Bel Pye, Reagan Reilly, Bryony Robinson, Beti Scott, Dorothy Sichi, Ailsa Sutcliffe, Heather Tulloch, Norma Wallis, Madge Welsh, Shirley Whiteside.

Battle of The Belvidere: Fighting the Fevers

Reaghan Reilly

I was drawn to the Diphtheria Casebook source because my mother contracted diphtheria as an infant in the 1920s. I picked Nurse Letty Merilees simply because I liked her name and because she was a Glaswegian, like me. The Two Marys can be found in the Servants Register. Both worked in the laundry for a comparatively long period and retired on pensions on 31 December 1914. My story is imaginative fiction, with facts sprinkled throughout.

~

Accipe signaculum doni Spiritus Sancti.

As a priest delivers the final blessing, I shed a silent tear for the parents in absentia and pray for Sophie's immortal soul. In less than twenty minutes, she will be dead. She is one-year-old and five twelfths – seventeen months.

This is the City of Glasgow Fever Hospital, also known as The Belvidere, Ward twenty-three: the diphtheria ward. It is summer 1917. May twenty-ninth. My birthday.

Little Sophie's parents cannot be here today; they are forbidden to enter. Isn't that the saddest thing you ever heard? But, as war rages all across Europe, we are waging our own battle here to stop many fever germs from spreading to the city outside the hospital walls.

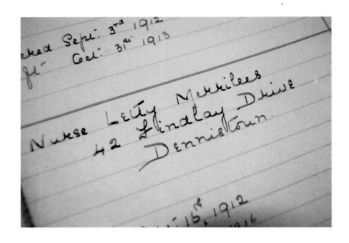

And, in order to do so, we cannot allow outsiders to enter the wards.

Oh! Did you hear that? That's Sister shouting on me. I'm needed elsewhere... That's me, by the way, Nurse Merilees. Letty Merilees from Dennistoun, Glasgow. Pleased to make your acquaintance.

Everything a fever patient comes into contact with is burned – their clothes, their personal effects, everything. I cannot even give Sophie's beloved dolly to her mother; it will be incinerated as it is almost surely riddled with fever germs. The bodies... there are some who think they should also be burned. *(Nurse Merilees crosses herself.)* The bodies are given a decent Christian burial; unless they're Jewish, of course. *(Beat.)* No one is immune.

The Belvidere is a specialist hospital now, but it wasn't always so. It was originally a temporary hospital to take care of the extra patients from Kennedy Street, but when fevers started to spread from there into the nearby tenements, the whole area got sick and people were panicking, so the council extended the Belvidere, upgraded it and it became the permanent fever hospital.

Look; see this window? Round, like a porthole on a ship. That's to stop dust from settling so that germs can't live on the window sill. And listen; *(she knocks on the window)* hear that? Thick, dense, double-glazed. Keeps everything in, so the fever germs can't escape into the community. Unfortunately, it keeps the heat in too. This place is sweltering and we could not open a window if we wanted. They are made that way.

Now, if you will excuse me, I must get these sheets to the laundry... Oh, no, when I said earlier that everything was destroyed I did not mean the bedding. Good linens cost a lot of money.

I hope the Two Marys have not slept in for their early shift. The Two Marys are the best laundry maids here and the longest serving. They are also quite the gadabouts and I am sure they were out quaffing a gin or two last evening, seeing as it was pay day.

All workers of Glasgow Corporation and Parish Council are paid on a Thursday and that includes everybody at the Belvidere except the doctors; they are salaried.

It will not be the first time I have had to chap them up; the Two Marys, that is... yes, of course... they live in hospital housing on the grounds of The Belvidere; we all do – laundry, kitchen staff, nurses, ward sisters

– even the matron and the doctors. It is all part of the plan to keep the fever germs from spreading outside the hospital. And, so far, it seems to be working.

That is why the hospital site is so big. You know it runs from Parkhead all the way down to the Clyde? We have over 300 patients and almost as many staff. Although... at least as staff you are guaranteed a bed. It is not unusual for us to have many more patients than there are beds. It is also not unusual for staff to become patients.

Take Gertie, for instance, Nurse Gertrude Chalmers. She has spent more time admitted to the wards than nursing the afflicted, poor girl. She has contracted polio, diphtheria and typhus. It is a wonder she is still with us. She must have the constitution and strength of a Clydesdale, though you would not think it to look at her; slip of a girl, pale and wan.

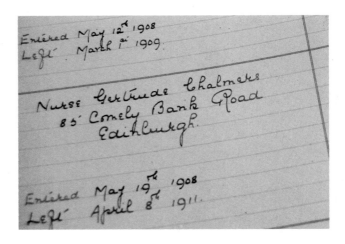

There's the Ward Sister calling on me again. I really must get on. It will not do to get a black mark against my name in the Ward Book. Matron is very stern and a stickler for discipline.

It is not only the kitchen and laundry staff that are known to slip out of an evening; the nurses take their fair share of evening refreshments out of bounds. The trick is to slip back onto hospital grounds again without being caught. Luckily, I am a canny lassie from the East End of Glasgow and not some teuchter from the Western Isles like a lot of the girls here, so I have not been caught and I intend to keep it that way.

If Matron does catch you, you get an awful dressing down and you will hang your head in shame for a week. Not to mention the caustic comments she puts down in the Ward Book and that goes on your permanent record.

You should see some of the things she has written about the nurses, and the laundry maids get even shorter shrift – but that is a story for another time. I'd better get these sheets to the laundry now and get on with my other duties. God bless you and keep you safe and may you never have to pay a visit to this place again.

Making a Difference

Kathryn Munro

My inspirations were Nurse Annie Ralston from the Nurses' Register – a professional, academic nurse at the start of her nursing career; and a picture of the tennis courts at the Belvidere, signifying peace and tranquility amidst the disease and suffering. The diseases the hospital dealt with also made me think about epidemics in more modern times. The last report of smallpox by natural causes, for example, was in Somalia in 1977. The World Health Organisation declared it eradicated in 1980, the first disease to be fought on a global scale. Around this time, a new disease was emerging: AIDS. Dedicated people like Annie Ralston are now searching for cures and ways to alleviate suffering and distress amongst the age-old phenomenon of prejudice and ignorance.

～

I got a letter today, from my cousin Mary, who is a nurse in Belvidere Hospital. She sent me a photograph which showed the nurses playing tennis in the hospital grounds. After working fourteen-hour days, and with one afternoon off a fortnight, it is good to see that there is some respite from caring for the sick and vulnerable.

When Mary left home to go to work at the fever hospital, all the family had severe misgivings. It was not the path her father wanted her to follow. Nursing was not for the faint-hearted, but she was strong and noble in her desire to make a difference in the lives of others. Rough, domestic chores were done by servants, but it was still a hard job physically and emotionally. Being quarantined for months when there were outbreaks led to loneliness and isolation. Thank goodness she had her fellow nurses for company and decent lodgings in the Nurses' Home.

We were lucky to grow up in a good area, west of Glasgow. It was not so fortunate for those living in the crowded unsanitary slums and hovels next to the River Clyde. That's where the fever outbreaks originated. In 1871 Glasgow Town Council built Belvidere Infectious Diseases Hospital, and not before time! It has served the population well, though at times overcrowded and understaffed.

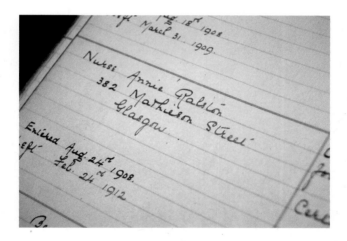

Not long ago, my family were fortunate to survive unscathed the smallpox epidemics of 1900 and 1902. Smallpox causes terrible suffering and the mortality rate is very high, especially in children. Those who do recover are often left with disfiguring scars from the spots and pustules; blindness and general debility. People living too close together in the slums had no means to escape the spread of disease and their infected bodily fluids contaminated each other and their possessions. At Belvidere, five temporary pavilions were erected in the grounds to provide more beds. Yes, this is what I feared my cousin would get caught up in and we would never see her again...

But she has remained there for three years, receiving instruction on the wards and attending lectures. She was made a full member of staff after one year. Well regarded for her good character, she left to enrol in general training at the Royal Infirmary. For my cousin, the nurse, and all the others who dedicated their lives, I have the utmost admiration.

I also think about how another disease was caught in time. It was a doctor from the Belvidere who discovered that it was rats carrying the bubonic plague in the Gorbals in 1900 and not the poor, scapegoated by the ignorant. The biggest rats were the rich merchants bringing their cargo to the Clyde and distributing more disease and more misery.

Tea and Memories

Dorothy Sichi

My inspiration was an entry for Nurse Christina McLennan in the Nurses' Register. What attracted me was the fact that she was at the Belvidere for three separate periods from 1914-1919. I was intrigued by what was behind the pull she felt to the hospital. I was also attracted by the images of nurses at play in the grounds

~

Jack, would you have a look at this photograph I've just found in amongst the family snaps? I was looking for them to show Fiona. It's the one of us playing tennis at the Belvidere; I've been looking for this photograph for months; it must have got lost in our last tidy. My... when I look at it, I can take myself right back there again. We did have special times amidst the hard work and endless hours of looking after sick people and keeping those diseases at bay!

Have a look at this, Fiona. Now, who can I remember? I am sure that is Jessie MacInnes and there's Margaret Somerville. Jack, you remember them; we were all good friends. You and I hardly knew each other at that time; I always thought you wanted to ask me out, but were not brave enough! Can you imagine your Granddad being like that, Fiona? He was quite shy.Do you remember the first shift we did together, Jack? It was a last minute change because some staff had absconded and we were put on the ward together. We were admitting that family from Maryhill;

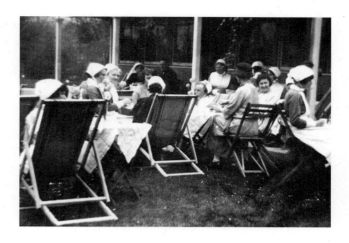

they all had whooping cough.

Do you remember, Jack? They were such poor souls and undernourished; I thought you were so kind the way you dealt with them. It was so sad when the youngest child didn't make it; her mother was heartbroken, Fiona. Yet your Granddad did manage to calm her down. She was just one of many grieving mothers that we saw, but she sticks in my mind because of your Granddad's kindness.

I do wonder at times, Fiona, how I coped with the duties; it's hard to believe that I was only sixteen when I joined the Belvidere in 1914. The job was really tiring in the early days; I struggled to get to grips with the tasks and the flood of people that would come in with all sorts of terrible ailments. Yet, over time, it became routine and not too difficult. Of course, time off was always used wisely. During the summer we spent time outside, as you can see, often chatting or playing tennis or walking in the grounds as we were not allowed off the premises. During winter we often read or did needlework. The men, of course, would have games nights. Such a different workplace now for doctors and nurses. When you start your training, Fiona, you must tell me what it's like!

Towards the end of the first year at Belvidere I became restless and went off to work in the Belgian Home for Refugees for the 'Corporation'. That was because I thought it would be more glamorous nursing Belgian soldiers rather than ordinary Glaswegians! Your Granddad still hadn't noticed me, so that was another reason for leaving! But I didn't last long though, did I, Jack? I came back to the Belvidere because I did miss the camaraderie, even though many staff didn't stay that long. We worked together as a team and it did feel that we were making a difference.

Le[ft] Left August 16ᵗʰ 1917.

N   Sister Christina Mc Lennan
            Station House
                Balmole
                    Stirlingshire.
    Age 32.   Father
    Entered Jan. 12ˢᵗ 1914   Insured.
    Left: April 6ᵗʰ 1915.   Vaccinated 1910.
    Re-entered – 31ˢᵗ July, 1919.   Protestant: U.F.
    Left – 31ˢᵗ October 1919
        Sister May Adams

I was also interested in seeing your Granddad again, Fiona, hoping that he may ask me out. But then, Jack, you were more interested in Helen Hunter? Oh yes you were. I really did not understand what you saw in Helen; she was selfish and superior. She pulled the wool over your eyes. Matron never liked her either; she was lazy and left all the dirty jobs to the other nurses. So, what did I do this time, Fiona? I applied for a military service post in France at the start of 1915! That was me all over; reckless and seeking adventure when I couldn't get my own way. I stayed there until the end of the war, as I did enjoy looking after those soldiers who fought bravely for our country, and there were so many that died, such a terrible loss of life, my dear.

I think it was the middle of 1919 that I returned to the Belvidere once again. Well, if I'm honest, I was curious to see if your Granddad was still there and not involved with that Helen one! And, of course, he was still there, working very hard but not emotionally involved with anyone. We struck up a great friendship straight away. So I was right, Fiona, he did like me after all!

The work was still hard at the Belvidere, but after the war there was more expertise and better advances in medicine. We worked long shifts, Jack, didn't we? We witnessed many sick people and some dreadful illnesses. Patients often died but many did survive because of the improved treatment.

We were married in the registry office soon after, then decided to apply to a private clinic in London and we were accepted, Fiona! Talk about moving fast: we did set tongues wagging at the Belvidere!

This photograph has sparked many memories for us, Jack, and it's very poignant to think that Fiona here is about to start nursing, but in such a different environment from ours all those years ago.

I think the Belvidere will be pulled down eventually, as it's a really old building even though it's still being used as a nursing home. I must tell your mum, Fiona, not to think about putting us in an old nursing home like that. Your Granddad and I want one of those new fangled ones with all the mod cons!

Now, where is my nurse's badge, I want to give that to you, Fiona, as a keepsake for you starting at university. Why don't you put the kettle on for us all, Fiona. We can have a cuppa, look through some more photos in time for you catching your train home? It's been lovely having you visit us again.

Witness Statement

Gail Addis

My inspiration was the distressing post mortem report of Mary Agnes Cameron and the on-going struggle to keep abortion safe and legal – we are very lucky in the UK, compared with elsewhere in the British Isles and the world.

~

High Court of Justiciary,
Glasgow
5th April 1923

Witness statement for the case of Mary Agnes Cameron (deceased)

Witness name: Jean Cameron Wilson

Date of Birth: 3rd September 1892

My name is Miss Jean Cameron Wilson. I am thirty years old. I am employed at Belvidere Hospital as a Staff Nurse. I have worked for the past eight years in Ward 16 which is the Puerperal Fever Ward. I am making a statement in lieu of a court appearance due to ill-health.

The deceased, Mary Agnes Cameron, was my young cousin. I had not seen her for nine years prior to the night that Dr Quigley arranged for her admission to Ward 16. That would have been the

General Peritonitis —

Mrs Cameron 28 yrs.
Ward XVI East.
Died 29th Nov., 1913.
Pm. 30th Nov. 1913

The cadaver is that of a well nourished female
Pm lividity well marked.

Chest.   No free fluid in chest and no adhesions
Both lungs show slight hypostatic congestion at back
Heart and pericardial sac appear normal except that
the cardiac muscle is soft and somewhat fatty
Valves healthy

Abdomen   The abdomen is much distended
and there is purulent fluid free both in the
abdominal cavity and in pelvis
Intestines appear healthy. Appendix normal
The uterus is greatly enlarged. On section
the mucosa lining the cervix is seen to be
gangrenous. The cavity of uterus is clean except
in a small area in each cornua where
are some small shreds of placental tissue
remaining

Liver   is enlarged and somewhat fatty.
Spleen   is soft, enlarged, and of the septic
Kidneys   appear normal
Pancreas   normal
Bladder   normal.
Tubes   There is evidence of extension
of septic mischief from the uterus via
the tubes to the abdominal cavity.
Head   not examined —

22nd of August 1922.

She was such a bonny wee child, ten years younger than me. I remember Aunt Jessie bringing her to visit us in Burnside, pushing the pram up the hill from Rutherglen. I'd play with her in the garden, pretending she was my dolly, but she was no dolly! A wee scamp even then! They never had two pennies to rub together, but we did our best to help. When the Quigleys needed a maid for yon big house, whatsit, aye "Rostrevor" in Clincarthill, I made sure Mary applied, although she was just out of school and only fourteen. I wish I'd never bothered now, but how was I to know how she'd turn out?

Dr Francis, I mean, Dr Quigley, Dr Francis Quigley, phoned the hospital switchboard at 9 o'clock in the evening with a message that he was bringing in a case of puerperal fever. It was very unusual for one of our doctors to bring in a patient, as they usually came by ambulance from the Royal or the Victoria Infirmary. He told me that he had spoken to Dr Archibald, the Medical Superintendent, as this was a very special case. I thought it was a bit odd, but was too busy to pay much heed.

I made up a bed near the door, with the screens drawn, so as not to disturb my patients and their babies. I was busy settling them down for the night when a car came to the door. I sent Nurse Baillie, the probationer, to help Dr Quigley bring the patient in. He said not to bother the House Officer, he would clerk the patient in himself.

He brought the case sheet to my desk to prescribe

some whisky for the patient. I should explain that whisky is given routinely to patients with puerperal fever when they become agitated. Then he said, "Sit down, Jean, I've something to tell you. I'm glad that it's you on duty tonight."

I wouldn't have recognised her! I'd not seen her in four years – since the disgrace – Aunt Jessie wouldn't have her name mentioned. All we knew was that she'd suddenly left service for the Quigleys and "gone to the country to work." There was nothing we could do. Whenever we mentioned her, Aunt Jean said, "She's no child of mine," and clammed up.

Mary was delirious; her temperature was 105 and her pulse 110. She looked anaemic (pale), and cachectic. (That means thin, undernourished.) She was restless, in a lot of pain, and holding her lower abdomen.

It was just dreadful. She was filthy; covered in vermin. And the smell that came from her – it was the smell of death; putrid. I did what I could for her. She had to be changed all the time... I'll never forget it. This was no 'puerperal fever'...

I tried to talk to her and ask her where the baby was, but she didn't recognise me, and was in a great deal of distress. Dr Quigley kept saying that he'd speak to me later. After she'd had the whisky she started to babble, and was saying things like "I'm no havin' it", "You"... or it might have been "Hugh"... "forgive me" and calling for her mammy.

I held her poor filthy, wee hand and begged her forgiveness. I asked her "Who did this to you, wee Mary?' I guessed that she was one of those cases where there's no baby, and you can tell when you're bathing them that there never was going to be one, if you catch my drift: weepy and vague about dates. Diagnosis "puerperal fever" and no questions asked. All hunky dory – as long as they live. Poor wee Mary had left it too late...

The next morning she rallied a little and her mind began to clear. I think she knew me, and I asked her who had done this. "She's a guid wummin. She helped us afore. I'm no tellin yous." She said something about "The Bellgrove", I'm afraid that is all she told me.

A guid wummin indeed! A bloody murderer! Taking advantage of desperate young girls, and killing them – Never heard of Professor Lister just up the road – filthy practices! I thought I'd seen the last of it after the war – we had a lot of 'puerperal fever' and other infections

*to deal with then – all those Jocks and Tommies coming
from the Broomielaw.*

*She asked for her maw, Aunt Jessie, and Dr Hugh – Dr
Francis Quigley's younger brother. I couldn't bring
myself to tell her that both are dead. Aunt Jessie left us
last year, and poor Dr Hugh was killed in a dressing
station near Albert in the second Somme – so close to the
end of the Great War. I told her that she'd be seeing them
both soon. That wasn't really a lie, was it?*

Mary passed away that afternoon, about 3 o'clock.
(Dr Quigley will have written the exact time on the
death certificate).

*I asked Nurse Baillie to help me lay her out. I took those
foul sheets to the sluice, and stood there, staring out the
window until I couldn't see the corporation reservoir for
tears. I was greeting and praying to the good Lord for
her soul, and for mine.*

Later, it was perhaps about 4 pm, as the teas were
finished, I heard Dr Quigley and Dr Archibald arguing
as they walked towards the ward, past the kitchens.
Dr Quigley was saying that he must call the Fiscal
to get a post mortem, for Mary's sake, and for the
others. "To stop this foul practice", I think was the
phrase. I wanted her to be left in peace then, but now
I understand it was for the best, as I have heard what
was in the report.

*He took me aside a few days later and showed me it –
uterus ruptured and torn to shreds – to shreds! That will
haunt me all my days.*

Dr Quigley told me that the cause of death was peritonitis due to abortion. Here ends my testimony.

Jean Cameron Wilson

Dated 5th April 1923

I hope that some good will come of this, and thank God that Aunt Jessie had gone to a better place before now. Goodness knows what Dr Hugh would have had to say. He was awful fond of Mary...

The Struggle of a Good Nurse

Jo Gray

I was inspired to write about Nurse Agnes Wallace from the nursing records because her conduct with children was recorded as questionable and that intrigued me. Her entry raised so many questions – especially why she needed supervision, even though she was regarded a good nurse, and what it was that made her resign. Using research into the symptoms of the fevers and the role of women in World War I, as well as the cause of puerperal fever, I wove a story for Agnes and her peers based on true names and life events.

~

I know I'm a good nurse. But I'm not like Helen. She's an *excellent* nurse. Yes, I know I attended all my lectures for years. And, although I got my nursing certificate eventually, she got top marks in all her exams, and has got into Bristol Royal, as you know, to do General training. I'm going nowhere, Sister.

In the four years I've been here I've picked up every fever possible; that's all I've done. I've been so ill. It's no life. Please don't shake your head. I'm not exaggerating! I've had chickenpox, scarlet fever, enteric fever, measles, diphtheria – which I nearly died from because I could hardly breathe. I've only just recovered from meningitis, as you know. To learn what I've said and done in my confusion is humiliating. I love children and can't bear to see them suffer without their mothers. I was not wrong to give them

a good nurse but required super-vision, not sure about her with children.
Resigned.

kisses and cuddles. I wasn't. They had no one. Who could play with them if not a nurse?

Before you suggest it, that's not how I contracted so many fevers. Helen has had just as many, and she's as hard as giving a box of nails to a baby. I'm sorry.

Please don't tut me. Even an excellent nurse like Helen has not escaped pregnancy and has nearly died from childbed fever. What? Childbed fever or puerperal fever, puerperal sepsis... it's all the same, you know what I mean. Well, anyway, I think far too many of us have experienced it. Considering that in the 1840s Dr Holmes suggested better hand-washing techniques by staff during birth could reduce the amount of deaths by half, I am distressed to hear of yet another puerperal sepsis death due to an abortion. As you know, I have tried to keep myself a good nurse and secretly had an abortion myself, at great pain and expense. I thought I'd got off lightly until ten days later when I began to get excessive soreness in my womb.

Nurse Helen M. Adamson
Adele Crescent
Motherwell.

Entered Nov. 17th 1908
Left Sept. 30th 1912

Nurse Agnes Wallace
Long Calderwood
East Kilbride.

Entered Nov. 18th 1908
Left July 1st 1912

Nurse Nellie Wotherspoon
14 Grafton Street
Glasgow.

Combining that with the terrible chills, thirst and another fever of 104, it was too much. I thought I was going to die for my sins.

Being in here I could be hidden away, but with all the newspapers and the court case following this recent death, my new man is not willing to risk an abortion. William would like me to keep this one, Sister.

So I am resigning. Yes I am. I will work my notice. But I'm worried about my health and the health of my baby, working in these conditions. It's not right. I wish my nerves had been so bad that I couldn't have stood the wards. That way I would have left four years ago, like Nurse Wotherspoon. You know, Nellie now has a job as a typist in the civil service? If only I could have been like her. She has a safe job earning over £2 a month. I have no health, no job, no money, and no life. I could die from having this baby.

No, I'm not being too dramatic. I resign.

I Didnae Want Tae Be A Nurse

Tracy McPherson

The inspiration for my monologue was a picture of a young nurse. I also found some nurses' names when doing research and one stuck in my mind; nurse Agnes Cowie Hamilton. There wasn't much information on her, just that she was there from 1912 and left in 1915. She was dismissed and branded unsatisfactory and dangerous. I thought she should be allowed to give her own version of events. Maybe she wasn't dangerous, just a little mischievous and misunderstood. So I gave her a voice.

~

I fought tae lift ma heed fae the pillow. I felt the springs dig intae ma skin and perch between ma ribs. I peered oot the windae. The clumps of big, white fluff floating in the sky met in the middle like curtains hiding us away fae the world. Just then, the door sprung open an' thudded against the wall.

"Right, get up, you." She scowled. Her eyes wis staring through us. The hair on her top lip danced as she scrunched up her face. I could hardly see her for the sweat running intae ma eyes. "I'm no' well... I've got a fever," I telt her.

"Just move," she said. I shuffled tae the end of the bed, swinging masel' up. I wisnae going tae tell her about the bottle the janny sneaked us. Me, him and ma pal, Jeanie, were drunk, we were whizzin' aroon' the room tae the imaginary music.

Then the smell caught the back of ma throat. It wis sweet at first, then sour, an' it wis unbearable. It wis deed flesh. It made us gag. It wisnae the first time I've been sick since coming tae work here; I didnae want tae be a nurse in the first place. It wis ma da who sent me here; said I wis getting a lot of attention fae the boys. Well, I didnae mind putting on my frock and my red lipstick, a wee bit of powder puff, that's true. The Matron took ma make up when I arrived. I say that as if it's a prison here. It's no' but it feels like it. Kaiser Bill wouldnae huv a look-in wae our Matron. I wish they'd send *her* tae war. She disnae like me... I think it's 'cause the gentlemen seem tae take a liking to me. I'm chatty an', I'd say, young and mere attractive.

As I walked doon the corridor, a wheezing sound echoed aroon' a room tae the left. I popped ma head round the door, just tae see. Lovely mop of dark curly hair: what a handsome guy, even covered in blisters. 'Sergeant' it said, aside his bed. His lips were white and his skin looked like it wanted to escape fae his face. I wis smiling; I couldnae help it. His eyes wir so dark that my tummy flipped. He must have been sent back from the front only to catch the smallpox in Glesga. It wis rife. I think we've all had it. Some of us huv had it twice.

Aye, aye, I'm gettin' tae the point. It wis just efter that... It wis roasting. Ma pinny wis soaking; it wisnae ma most attractive day, let's just say.

We had maistly women in that ward; just a few men asides the Sergeant. A wee old woman, Mrs Johns, had just died. Lovely, she wis, stayed aside us for years. Her man wis called up... don't know who wis watchin' her weans. Wae the heat, you could smell her. I'm surprised there wisnae maggots everywhere. Do you know, they left her for days. They wouldnae like us telling you that, eh? She wis getting better. She wis meant tae be goin' hame. Then she jist died all of a sudden. Why you no' asking them aboot her?

Awrite, I'll tell ye. The doctors an' the Matron sit doon an' huv dinner about five-ish. They huv their fancy plates an' a wee bevvy. Our plates are like an old tin bowl. No' fit for ma dug. I can huv a fancy plate and a wee drink when the Professor askes me tae his room. He's nice tae me... sometimes! He sneaks me ma make-up and lets me wear it fir that night. I don't like it when he kisses us, though. I wis lucky that the Matron came in, as I didnae want tae huv sex. Somebody had jist died! The Matron's look wis enough, so I ran oot the door. They didnae notice the wee bottle I'd pinched fae the Professor's room. Me and Jeanie were gonnae huv another party tae ourselfs.

Fair maid.

Very good ma

Very good wor

Good worker.

: 7th/16   Unsatisfactory

Good worker, bad temp

a. Very good m

good worker, left - to h

good worker.

The next day, the Matron wis on the warpath. Looking for me, especially. Must have been 'cause she caught us in the Professor's room, I thought. He invites all the young nurses tae his room. Maybe she found ma letter tae ma Da, asking if I can come hame, as I telt him whit it wis like here.

Well, she found me. Her face seemed soft an' she wis smilin'. She put her arm aroon' ma shoulder. "Come with me, pet." I smiled back at her an' her eyes seemed tae sparkle. She pointed tae a room. "You're working in there today, lovely."

I wis stuck on the spot. Ma feet had grown roots an' I couldnae move. What wis she being nice tae me for? I walked intae the room and ma mouth seemed tae hit the floor. The wee woman's body. Ma stomach wrenched an' I threw up. "You can clean that too," She laughed.

I sat in the corner an' gret, I just wanted ma mammy. I had tae get the room sorted. If it wisnae for Jennie who came and gie'd us a cuddle and a mask tae stop the smell... Well. She even stayed and helped us until she heard the Matron coming.

Matron stood in the doorway, smirking. The smell of her sweat and the wee woman's decomposing flesh wafted up ma nose and made ma eyes water. I tried ma hardest no' tae be sick; I didnae want her having the satisfaction. She had one hand leaning against the door, the sweat patches under her arms almost doon tae her ankles. I prayed she wis coming doon wae the fever. That old bag seemed tae be immune tae it. "Right, you're done doon here. You're needed up in the ward." I smiled, mirrorin' her, only *her* teeth were a yella colour; her red lipstick showed it up more.

Aye, I'm getting tae the point. I'm jist showing ye what it's like here, that's all. So I wis escorted tae the ward by the Matron. I wis tired; I'd been working all day withoot a break. I had tae check on ma Sergeant. I sat down beside him and damped his head wae a cold cloth. I swept his hair back fae his face. He'd been tossin' an' turnin' in his sleep. I'd talk tae him, tell him things: the weather, what I'd been up tae, aboot the Matron. Sometimes he just slept an' other times he'd blink his eyes. I think I wis in love wae him. The Matron hated it when I wis looking efter him. I sometimes looked in on him in the middle of the night tae make sure he wis awright.

Aye, right, that night? Matron wis her usual self, shouting at everyone. I just looked at the ground, then I couldnae be blamed for anything. She still picked on me, though. I wis shuggelling, legs crossed, holding masel in. She could see I wis burstin'. She made me stond there until I could feel the hot pee run doon ma leg and drip on the floor. That made her happy, seeing me covered in piss, shivering, scared and in tears. She wis a bully.

I wiped the smile aff her face that night. I put ma hands on her side and I shoved her as hard as I could. Well, did she no' go and slide on ma piss and skelpt her face aff the doorframe? There wis a big bruise on her eye and a cut on her nose. The blood wis everywhere. I ran. I felt like I wis floating; I telt her... Back in ma room I locked the door an' even scraped the cabinet along the floor up against the door, jist in case somebody tried tae get in.

I knew I wis in trouble. The Matron, of all people. She wis the meanest, nastiest and scariest person I know.

Well, I had tae prepare masel for her the next day. That morning I took a few swigs oot the bottle I got fae the Professor, jist tae calm ma nerves. I wis first on the ward. I helped give oot the medicine tae everyone. It gave me a wee ten minutes wae the Sargeant. I told him tae hurry up an' get better an' I'd let him take me oot.

Sorry, I'm getting tae it. I wis changing the bandages on Ina's legs – a right mess they were. Her legs were weeping nearly as bad as I wis last night. The Matron came in, looked at me an' smiled. I jist looked away an' concentrated on the bandages. I counted tae masel trying tae calm masel doon. Ma hands were shaking. I couldnae fasten the bandage until she left.

I walked past the Sargeant's room an' she wis in there. Ma stomach wis in knots. How dare she go in there? She wis standing over him as if tae talk tae him. She looked up and smiled. I turned ma head as if I hidnae seen her.

Next thing I hear is her screaming. I didnae want tae go back; her screech made me feel uneasy inside. I looked over ma shoulder. Everyone wis running towards the Sargeant. I felt the pounding in ma head as I scrambled along the corridor, just in time tae hear her say, "He's dead."

Everyone seemed tae be lookin' intae ma soul. I couldnae speak, but I wis screaming inside. Ma eyes welled up and the tears raced each other toward the floor. I felt empty. All I could see wis the Matron smirking at me. "Who gave him his medicine?" she shouted. I fell tae my knees, scraping them aff the cold, uneven tiles. I knew she'd given my Sergeant something and was trying to put the blame on me. I'd lost him and it wis all her fault. I'd never harm a hair on his head. Her, now... well, that's another matter.

An' that's all I've got tae say, officer.

The Zombie Ward

Anabel Marsh

At the first meeting of the Belvidere group, my eye was drawn to a picture from Glasgow Women's Library's Alice Bauchop collection showing a group of nurses and a young male doctor on a set of ward steps. In particular, I liked the woman in the middle with her arms crossed nonchalantly and a friendly smile on her face, so I was really lucky to find her again in a photograph in the Mitchell. Even better, her name, the name of the ward, and the year were all identified. After that, it was just a case of using a little imagination – and Wikipedia! I was worried that the term zombie might be an anachronism, but it was first recorded in 1819 and films featuring zombies have been a part of cinema since the 1930s. The former Nurse Watt is talking to her grandson sometime in the 1960s.

~

Och, Jimmy! You're not watching zombie films again, are you? I hate that kind of film. Why? They remind me too much of my worst days at the Belvidere. Look, this is me here – your Granny was Nurse Watt in those days. I was an innocent young lassie, just up from Kilcreggan. I'd never even *been* to Glasgow before, so it was a big shock – so busy! But I loved my work, most of the time. I'd always wanted to be a nurse.

We look happy here, don't we? That must have been... oh... 1923 I think. Sour-faced Dr Smith left in 1922 and we had the new young doctor. We all liked him. He was much more easy-going. And handsome! Look at his lovely hair. And, if it had been 1924, I don't think we'd have looked so cheerful. If I remember right, that was our worst year ever on Ward 14W.

Encephalitis Lethargica – that was the fancy name for what we treated. Sleepy sickness for short. Doesn't sound too bad, does it? Sleepy; lethargic. But it attacks the brain and some of the patients were left like statues. Couldn't speak. Couldn't move. It was an epidemic for about ten years – they say five million people around the world got it, and a third of them died. In one year we had more than 150 patients. Men. Women. Bairns. Fifteen died – one of them a little baby, not even a year old. That one nearly finished me.

Mind you, maybe the dead were lucky. Some of the ones that lived were never really alive afterwards. Conscious, maybe, but not awake. Like ghosts.

Or, like I said, zombies. No, Jimmy, I can never watch films with zombies.

Hetty McCadden Remembers

Norma K Wallis

I chose Hetty because I was a nurse in a gynaecology ward until I retired, so I knew a bit about these patients. They used to come into our ward with any neonatal problems as they would not be allowed back into a maternity ward in case of bringing in any infection. Sometimes the "wean" came in as well (we dreaded that because, although we all liked cuddling the "wean", it meant we had to help care for it as well, especially if "mum" went to theatre for a D&C and was not able to care for it on her own after an anaesthetic.

With thanks to the late Hetty McCadden.

~

Well... I never thought I would be telling you all this – such a long time ago, but I'll never forget any of it. So, here goes, you asked for it.

Me and Alec had eight weans aged fourteen, twelve, eight, four and wee Dorothy, just born. We lost three others. Tommy would be fourteen now; he died of the scarlet fever when he was only three. Teddy – he's just fourteen – followed his Da and Grandda down the pit. He gives me his wages every week and I give him half a crown back for pocket money.

George would be ten. He was never "right in the head" as they said, used to have fits. Then one day he didn't come round from one, "George", I shouted, "Wake up! Wake up!" I shook him till he rattled, but it was nae good. He died there in my arms, right in front of the fireplace. Emmy would be three, but she was stillborn. The cord was round her neck. They wouldnae let me see her, even though I wanted to. She was my bonnie little lass, they said, but I never got to see what she looked like. They say ye get over these things, but ye dinnae. It just fades away a bit.

Mary, age twelve, has grand ideas. Wants to work in the haberdashers where they sell all they fancy ribbons, bows, laces and pretty materials. She'll be lucky if she can get a job in one of they big hooses as a maid. She'll be leaving school this summer and will have to get a job to help pay for her keep. Albert, he's eight, wants to be a train driver, but I doot that will happen. He'll be doon the pit like the others. Wee Hetty, aged four, keeps changing her mind. At the moment she wants to be in the circus. We saw one once, came to the big Green they did. It was magic, so it was; all those girls in their spangly costumes showing all their legs. I said, "If ye think ye're going tae show everything, Hetty, ye've got another thought coming."

Now I've got another wean – I was hoping Hetty would be the last. Oh, well, you have to take what the good lord sends you. I hope Dorothy is the last, though. We have little enough money as it is, and now another mouth to feed. Anyway, when Dorothy was born, that was when it all went pear-shaped.

Everything went well with the birthing. My neighbour, Jessie McAllister, was the midwife round here and she and my sister Pearl delivered the wean. It was alright for the first few days. Jessie came round to check my belly and "doon below". Ye ken what I mean. Pearl helped with the washing, and with the other weans and got Alec and Teddy's dinner when they got home from the pit. I was caring for Dorothy and doing the housework.

Well, I was washing their pit clothes — real clatty they get – and I got this awfy pain in my belly. Doubled me up it did; worse than having the wean. But I managed as best I could, told myself it would be better in the morning. Well, I had a terrible night, what with the pain and feeding and changing the wean. Alec got up to go to work. "In the name of wee man, Hetty," he said, "that's some smell here, like something the cat dragged in." I then knew it was me!

I was really feeling poorly. I dragged myself up and about and got the weans off to school. When Pearl came round I felt even worse and she went for the doctor. Took a shilling from the Oxo tin on the mantelpiece for his fee, even though we could ill afford it. Well, that's when I was taken to the Belvidere.

Talking about me, so they were: "Well, you've all been here on this ward long enough. You, Doctor Cameron, tell me about this woman."

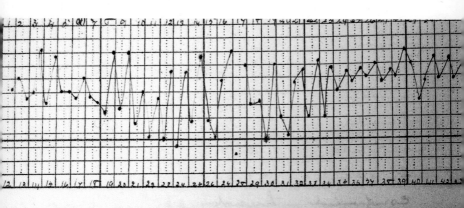

e.	Day of Illness	A.M.			P.M.			MOTIONS.	URINE.			
		Temp.	Pulse	Resp.	Temp.	Pulse	Resp.		Quantity	Sp.Grav.	React.	Albumen.
h	12ᵗʰ				102·2	112	26	3m	Urine incont		Acid	tra
2	13	103·	112	25	107·4	106	36	3m	1. Powder			

39

"Well, Sir," one of the young doctors started, "Mrs McCadden is aged 31. She delivered her eighth child – a natural birth – on 3rd October. She started feeling ill on the 12th October with severe left sided abdominal pain accompanied by a foul smelling discharge. On examination, she is a fat, well-nourished woman. Uterus and adnexae were normal. She had a temperature of 103F, pulse 105 and regular. We commenced daily douching with iodine solution and manipulation, which caused slight bleeding. There was no discharge otherwise. We continued this treatment and her pain lessened, temperature and pulse returned to normal and the discharge has now stopped. She was diagnosed as suffering from puerperal fever, probably due to poor hygiene and poor social conditions. I think she is ready for discharge home." The older doctor nodded. "That sounds like a good plan, Doctor Cameron. Sister, get this woman discharged."

Well! Fat, indeed? Well-nourished? I bet he never had a jeely piece for his dinner, or lived in a single end with a tap in the yard and a lavvy shared by six or eight families. It's alright for him in his big hoose.

Ye've nae idea what it was like in that there Belvidere. I remember it just like yesterday. It's as if I wisnae there and they were talking to the wall! They never spoke to me, nor hardly looked at me. I was just "that woman" lying in the bed. I didnae have a name. They didnae tell me what they were goin' to do with that there douching. It was bliddy sore having that thing pushed inside me. Not to mention my dignity – or lack of it, really. If they men knew what women had to put up with it might be a bit different! They nurses were frightened of the Sister; proper dragon she was. And the young Doctors were frightened of that Consultant, not to mention of the Sister as well.

The food was terrible, too. Most of the girls in there thought it was good – and I suppose it was, to them – and they could have as much as they wanted. They were poorly fed at hame, so it was understandable, but I wouldn't have put it in front of my Alec. I made sure he had a good hot meal when he came hame from the pit. Anyway, after aboot a week they let me go home. I swore there would be no more weans for me, and there weren't, but that was more luck than anything else. We didnae have the pill then. That was the best thing that ever happened for women, I say.

Well, Jenny, I bet ye never expected all that when ye asked me aboot how it was when I had all of they weans. And your Ma was the last. Now, my granddaughter is going to the Royal to train to be a nurse. I hope ye remember what I said and treat all of your patients with dignity and respect, not like it was those days in that there Belvidere, especially for us women when we have our weans. All the problems we get that men don't understand! But I'm sure you will think of my story. I am so proud of you. I know you'll do well. Off you go now, hen. And I wish you all the luck in the world.

Two Days in June

Louisina Currie

When I was first looking for a character for my monologue in what little documented accounts there were for the patients, nurses and staff at the Belvidere Hospital, the name Catherine Reynolds jumped out at me as she had the same name as a relative of mine. And the date she died was 3rd June, which is my birthday. The two together brought a great sadness over me. This little girl was twelve, taken into the hospital, but too late to save her. I am so glad to be remembering Catherine in this monologue as it means she will never be forgotten and her memory will live on. I wonder where her relatives are today. Belvidere hospital was part of my childhood; my sisters were both in the hospital for fevers. They survived and I think how things could have been different for Catherine if only, if only.

~

I feel so comfy in this big, clean bed. I can hear everything going on around me, but it's as if I'm underwater. The nurse is telling someone called Peggy who I am and that she should fetch my ma. She tells the other nurse that my name is Catherine Reynolds and that I'm twelve. I want to tell her that I'm nearly thirteen, but the words won't come. She tells Peggy to go and tell my Ma that I was found in Ballater Street and they brought me here, to Ward 23, Infectious Diseases. I don't know what Ward 23 is, or where it is, or how I got here.

Oh Ma! Ma will be angry; I know she will. She told me

Catherine Reynolds. 12 yrs

Adm. 1 June 1912 to Wd 23.
Cod⁼. T.B. Meningitis.
P.M. performed: 3rd June 1912.
Died   3rd June 1912.

Emaciated.

Heart. apparently normal.

Lungs. R Lung. A number of pleural adhesions.
numerous Tubercles in Apex & one or 2 caseous foci.

L Lung. Visceral pleura adherent to parietal in
practically it's entirety. These adhesions
broken down with much difficulty.
Apex entirely occupied with caseous foci, in
fact the whole of L. upper lobe is so affected.

Liver. some degenerated areas.

Spleen. no tubercles seen.

Kidneys. congested — otherwise practically
normal.

Brain. Convolutions flattened. Veins greatly
engorged. marked cushion of oedema beneath
medulla, pons & crura. Much matting of fibrous
tissues there. No pus seen anywhere.
Lateral ventricles appeared to contain fluid
under pressure.

to stay in bed, but how could I? She was struggling with wee Tommy, Sheila and that bundle on her back going to the steamie. I just thought I could go and help her as a wee surprise. I'm not sure how far I walked but I don't remember anything after my head started to go fuzzy.

How did I get here? Everything seems blurry but I feel so much better now: relaxed and not so hot, tucked up in this lovely bed. I'm so tired, though. Think I'll just sleep now as Ma will be on her way to take me home. I wonder if she can bring these nice, clean and comfy sheets with us.

I can hear the nurse telling Peggy to hurry, that I'm weak and that my body is too tired to fight.

She sounds sad. I want to tell her that I'm happy that Ma is coming, and that I just need to sleep for a while, but I can't.

I let the voices go.

I hope Ma comes soon.

Floppy and The Fever

Margaret Duffy

My stimulus for this piece was a combination of being in Belvidere in 1946 as a 4 year old and coming across the notes on a nurse whose report was excellent and who went to London to nurse Belgians. 250,000 Belgian refugees fled across the Channel in 1914 to escape the Germans.

~

When I was your age I had a toy rabbit just like that. What happened to him? Well, I was in hospital with scarlet fever... feeling very sleepy... "Why is the side of that cot down, Nurse?" The Sister's grumpy voice made me jump.

The nurse with the lovely brown eyes just like Mum's murmured, "Mary is almost five, Sister, and used to sleeping in a bed but all the beds are full." "Rules are rules, Nurse, put it up immediately." Nurse McLeod gave me a little wink as she obeyed. I didn't want to be a cry baby like the girl in the next cot who had cried all day for her mummy, so I hugged Floppy and wiped my eyes on his soft, furry ears.

Later, Nurse McLeod gave me some water and put cool cloths on my forehead. She called me a brave girl and said I could call her Nurse Mary once I could speak again. My throat was very sore and I could only whisper, but I tried to smile at her. I think maybe she liked me especially because we had the same name.

I opened my eyes the next morning to a ring of strange faces round my cot. Men in dark suits stared down at me. Nurse Mary leaned over me and gently eased the covers back, whispering that they were doctors and that they would help to get me better.

The clump of their shoes as they walked down the ward was very loud and their voices rumbled as they stopped and looked at all the girls and women in the ward and talked about them as cases. It was very confusing and I didn't understand why they were talking about us as though we were luggage and not by our names. But I was too tired to listen to them and, instead, snuggled into Floppy and watched bars of sunlight dancing across the room from the high windows.

For many days, I watched the sunlight move round the walls, gradually getting used to the strange mixture of smells of antiseptic, polish and boiled cabbage - smells which made me sick at first; listening to the squeak of nurses' shoes on the polished floor and the rustle of their starchy uniforms. I got to know the sound Nurse Mary's shoes made, as well as the fearsome squeal of the Sister's.

Some nights, the sounds of children sobbing woke me up, and Sarah in the next cot still cried a lot, but much more quietly now, as if she couldn't be bothered. One morning, I woke and Sarah's cot was empty. Nurse Mary was washing the cot and she looked very sad but smiled when she saw me watching her, bathed me with cool water and brought me some gruel.

One day, when I was feeling a bit better and could sit up, she came to me and said it was Saturday, "You've been in hospital for three weeks, my dear, and your mum and aunt are outside."

"Is this the first time they've come to see me?"
I asked.

"Oh no, Mary. They come every week but no one is allowed in because you're in quarantine."

My cot was quite near the entrance of the ward, with its heavy wooden doors with thick, rectangular glass panes at the top. I could just see two shadows and blurry faces and what might have been hands pressing on the glass.

"Look, Mary, they're waving to you. Smile and wave back. Show them you're getting better." I tried to smile and gave a little wave but I could feel my lip trembling, so I grabbed Floppy and squashed him to me.

The next week, Nurse Mary said she had some news for me; she was going away. There was a big war on and thousands of Belgium people came across the sea to escape. They were near to a city called London.

"So, you are going to London?" I asked her, clutching Floppy very hard.

"Near there. It's called Spring House. They need nurses and doctors."

"But *we* need you."

She smiled in that gentle way she had and stroked my hair. "I know, Mary, but you are getting better and there are a lot of nurses here. I think they need me more at Spring House."

I whispered to Floppy that the Belgians were very lucky to get our best nurse.

A few days after Nurse Mary finally left, Sister Fearsome appeared at my cot as I woke up. "Good news for you, child, you are going home today. You are clear of the fever now."

She told me my mum would collect me that afternoon. Later, a young nurse came with some clothes which were all new. I was very weak and needed help to put them on. Once I was dressed, she sat me down in a chair and stripped the covers off the cot. Then she held her hand out towards Floppy.

I stared at her, not understanding what she wanted. "He's to go!" she said.

Went to "Spring Hall" Home for Belgian Refugees
under Corporation of Glasgow, to take entire charge.
October 28" 1914. Returned to Belvidere
after three months & left for military serv.
April 6 1915.
Re-entered Belvidere ~ 31st July, 1919.
Left for Private work in London ~ 31st October, 19

"Go where?"

"In the incinerator... where all the personal belongings
have to go."

I cried for my poor Floppy, "Goodbye my darling,
you never did me any harm." I gave him a kiss and
a last hug.

Did I get another one?

Oh yes, but I never forgot Floppy.

The Ambulance

Mary Alice McLellan

My inspiration was the archive collection at Glasgow Women's Library where there are some photos and papers of Alice Bauchop, who was a nurse at the Belvidere. Her family had a connection to Bridgeton which is where I live and I wanted to write about her. She used to go out with the ambulances to pick up patients. I also wanted to have the little girl's house in Landressy Street because that is where Glasgow Women's Library is and I like going there.

~

The house is in Bridgeton. Not very far away. The patient is a five year-old girl. Her name is June. Will she survive until the ambulance gets there? I don't like it when we have to pick up children because it reminds me of when my sister died. And after that I had to wear black for two years and there were always lilies around the house. I hate lilies now. And I hate wearing black.

We got to the house in Landressy Street where the child was and went in the close. We went up two flights of stairs. The mother opened the door, crying. We went in. June was lying on the couch. I checked her over. She had a rash, a headache and a fever. It was smallpox. We all went downstairs with June and got in the ambulance. We sped through the streets. But when we got to Parkhead, the roads were full of people going to the football.

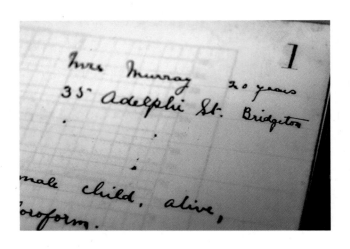

At last we got to the hospital. We took June to the smallpox ward and got her settled in. She was in hospital for three weeks and then was ready to go out to play again. I was glad that the girl didn't die because she reminded me of my sister.

What Did Your Granny Do In The War ?

Madge Welsh

Taking part in this project brought back memories of the only times in my life I'd ever been in in that hospital: the deaths of my parents when I was a teenager. So, finding out the history of Belvidere was, for me, a rather bittersweet experience, but one I enjoyed. I chose Margaret Nellson from a photo in the archive. The nurses all had such a stern look about them, but it's the kindness in someone's heart that matters and she chose to go into an environment where her own life was put at risk.

~

I remember it was just before my 80th birthday when you asked me if I could help you with a school project. "What did your granny do in the war?" was the question. This was 1964, I think, a few years ago now, mind you. "Which war?" I asked you. I was old enough to have survived both.

I sent you to fetch the old box from the cupboard: the one marked 'Peggy's Memories' and, as we looked through the old photographs, I was transported down memory lane. It had been many a year since I'd last looked at some of those images. The happy and sad memories contained within each one took me back to one of the hardest, yet happiest, periods of my life.

The first picture had me standing as straight as a dye in my pristine, starched nurse's uniform, looking very severe. November 1919 was the date on the back of the picture. In that picture, I am Margaret (Peggy) Nellson and that was when I began my working life as a nurse in Glasgow. I began my training at the nursing school at Belvidere Hospital in Glasgow. It had acquired a reputation for producing nurses of a high calibre and I trained under the tutelage of Sister Mary Buchanan; a strict, but extremely knowledgeable woman, who went on to mould me into a wonderful nurse.

I once told you some silly story about how I got into trouble for being late for work one day. I didn't want to tell you the bad stuff back then, but I'll tell you now you're older.

Belvidere was a permanent fever and smallpox hospital when I first went there to train and, within weeks of my arrival, an outbreak of smallpox started in Glasgow, which was an extremely unhealthy place at that time. The squalid conditions in which the overcrowded inhabitants had to live promoted the rise and spread of many diseases. Belvidere Hospital was built in rapid response to one such epidemic.

This city of my youth had many difficulties, with high levels of poverty and deprivation. With as many as ten or a dozen of us living in one room – jeez-o. Poor levels of hygiene and sanitation led to such outbreaks spreading like wildfire.

Sometimes, whole families would be admitted to the wards. I worked on the female ward and, one Sunday, a lady by the name of Mrs Agnes Bain and her daughter, Nancy, were admitted to the hospital showing signs and symptoms of smallpox: fever, a rash of red spots on her tongue and in her mouth. Those spots would change into sores that would break open and spread large amounts of the virus into the mouth and throat. Then a rash would appear on the skin, starting on the face, and spreading to the arms and legs, and then to the hands and feet. Usually, it spreads to all parts of the body within twenty-four hours. As the rash appears, the fever begins to decline, and the person should start to feel better, but not Mrs Bain. After nine days fighting her illness, she died. She was the first patient I'd lost in this outbreak and it had terrible impact on me.

It made me realise how vulnerable I was to catching a fever myself. In fact, some of my fellow nurses and doctors had already succumbed to the virus.

Living and working in the Belvidere at the beginning was enjoyable but also fraught with danger, as I was to find out later. We were given our own rooms in the nurses' quarters, which seemed luxurious to a young woman who shared a room at home with her three sisters. Having somewhere of my own to go once my shift was over, somewhere where I could lock out death and dying, helped me cope with such an emotionally draining job.

After five years of what most people would call being lucky, my luck finally ran out when there was another outbreak of smallpox in Glasgow. It was 1925 and, once again, I was on the ward looking after several patients when I suddenly began to feel ill and those tell-tale red spots appeared on my tongue. Within hours, I was a patient on my own ward. I don't remember too much of what happened to me but others told me I was in and out of consciousness for over a week. Apparently, I came very close to death. When I was well enough to leave, I returned home to recuperate and, within six months, I'd met your granddad. We fell in love and married a year later.

Unfortunately, despite all my training and years as a nurse, once I married Peter I had to give up the job I loved for the man I loved.

...	Meas...	Meas...
...han	Diphtheria	Meas...
...derson	Measles	Measles
"	Measles	Measles
Walker	Scarlet	Scarlet
a. K. b	Wh. Cough	Wh. Cough
Davidson	Diphtheria	J. Diphtheria
Lyon	Diphtheria	J. Diphtheria
" Millar	Scarlet?	Measles
" Napier	G. Measles	G. Measles
" Rankin	Mem: Croup	J.J. Diphtheria
" McFarlane	Enteric	Enteric
" Hardy	Scarlet	Scarlet
" Duncan	G. Measles	G. Measles
Str.	Turner	Scarlet	Scarlet
stitute " Lyon	Diphtheria	J. Diph...
...e. " Ballantyne	Scarlet	Scarlet
Rd. " Ledgerwood	Scarlet	Sc...
n Rd. Str. Morrin	Diphtheria	Diphtheria...
ld Str. " Campbell	Measles	Measles
...tern Rd. " Walker	Scarlet	Scarlet
Str. ...t Kaign...	Puer...	wh...

The Gossip

Jo Gray

I was inspired to write about Staff Nurse Florence Philips because
she was noted to be a chronic grumbler. Coupled with reading the
servants' records and basically feeling that, in most cases, the worst
aspects of their character were recorded, I thought to write about
the servants from the perspective of a complaining staff nurse
would be an amusing way to tell the names of true life women
and their supposedly bad qualities!

~

Isn't this staff room a tip, Margaret? That Jenny
Dunnigan is a dirty girl. You just can't get the staff
in here these days. Just look at the colour of this
mug! And the other Jenny isn't much better. Such a
stupid girl.

I know. I miss Annie, too. She was a good ward maid.
A rarity. This Bella Kennedy is not satisfactory at all.
She asked me earlier where the bed pans were kept.
She's been with us about a month. What do you think
she's been doing? Apparently, not taking the piss!
Exactly. Well, did Mary Irvine tell you she's leaving to
be married? Some poor farmer up north is getting
her. I pity the animals when you consider how she
cleaned in here.

Talking of foul, I was doing the rounds earlier and you
could smell the feet off Smith as soon as you walked
in the ward. And you wouldn't believe it, but when I

pulled her up for it, McPhilamy butted in to defend her. Such an objectionable woman. I really hope she runs away! Yes, hopefully I make her life miserable enough. By the way, I've asked Margaret Shaw to resign. She's had more sick days than toilet breaks. And you're right, she *has* got a weak bladder.

That's another good one ran away. Alice went out on pass and hasn't returned. I think Sister Williams is too soft on them. She's all pals. No good as a ward manager. Well, that's me finished my cuppa; I'd better head back to the chaos. The last thing I've been meaning to say, Margaret, is that I can't stand young Agnes Murphy. She's a chronic grumbler!

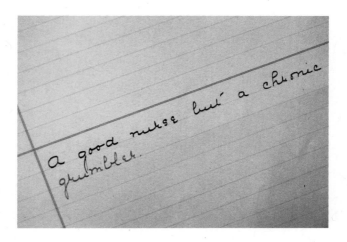

ft to
Good wa

Good wor

Dirty girl.

Stupid girl.

ut of a

Lucky Sister

Donna Moore

I took as my inspiration the staff records of the maids and nurses. I found these records fascinating. Long columns of names, whereabouts in the hospital they worked, when they joined, when they left and a few words about their conduct or why they left: "Bold girl", "Ran away", "Dirty, troublesome girl", "Returned to her husband. Good girl", "Got out, came back drunk", "Asked to resign because she would insist on talking to porters". Voiceless women summed up in a few words; nothing about who they really were or what their lives were really like. Amongst them were Martha Cross, who worked as a ward maid from 1914-16 and whose record states "Good worker. Left to go to munitions work"; and Nurse Gertrude Chalmers, whose record says: "Contracted all the diseases, some of them twice. Was on duty about 4 months out of 3 years." Gertrude, you were a more dedicated woman than I would ever have been. I would have handed in my notice after the first bout of typhoid.

～

Well, you were right, weren't you, Martha? What was it you said? "Ella, with your luck, you'll catch every disease going." I was a bit put out at the time. You were always the lucky one, ever since we were children, and you just kept rubbing it in. You told me I shouldn't come to work at the Belvidere because I'd just get ill. I thought you just didn't want your little sister hanging around spoiling things for you. After all, you'd been there for over a year, and you hadn't caught anything, had you? Even when you and one of the patients sneaked over the wall during the cholera epidemic and went to the pub. You did make me laugh with your tales. That was one of the reasons I wanted to work there. And you always seemed so happy, and had all that money to spend on clothes and going out to the dancing.

And you never caught anything in all the time you were there, did you? You were the lucky one, you kept telling me. Me, now... well, if there's something to be tripped over, or walked into, or fallen down, then you can bet your last shilling that I will trip over it, walk into it or fall down it. So, it stands to reason that I got the typhoid. Twice. Ooh, I was so ill. I never thought I'd pull through that. Six weeks I was in that time. I don't remember too much, to be honest. But I do remember that you would come onto the ward every day to see me, even though you weren't really allowed to. If Matron had caught you, you'd have been in trouble, even though we were sisters. She was always a stickler for the maids keeping to their assigned wards. But the nurses let you in when you charmed them, just like you've always been able to do.

After I got better, they told me that you would sneak onto the ward every day and bathe me. Even when you weren't on duty they said you'd be there, sometimes for hours. They said you lifted me in and out of that bath so gently, sponging me down and massaging my limbs. And never a care for your own health. And yet, you were still lucky. I was so glad you didn't get it too.

And then a month after that I caught scarlet fever. I don't even know how I caught that, that wasn't even my ward to clean. I think it was one of the other maids who gave it to me. You told me then I should leave, get a different job. I was so stubborn, though. The more you pushed, the more I insisted on staying. "I've had typhoid and scarlet fever," I said. "What else could go wrong?"

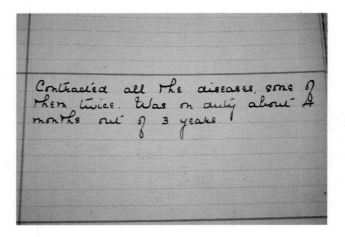

Contracted all the diseases, some of them twice. Was on duty about 4 months out of 3 years.

blisters started appearing, I thought it was just heat from the machines in the laundry, but you took me straight to Matron. And you were right. And there I was, whipped right back into a ward. I think I must have spent time in every one of those wards in my year at the Belvidere. If I wasn't cleaning them, I was a patient in them.

Well, that was enough for you. You looked after me then, too. Spent nights sleeping in a chair by my bed, holding my hand. And your luck held out. But, after I got better, you told me you were leaving, to get a better job in the munitions factory, and that I should come with you. The pay was better, you said. Less than half of what the men were paid, of course, but still better than at the Belvidere. And you wanted out before your luck changed. And... well, as always, you were worried about me.

And I did think about it, I really did. Everyone was so proud of you munitionettes, doing your bit for the war effort. I was just about ready to hand my notice in at the Belvidere but you started turning yellow. Yellow! It was the chemicals you used, you said. Trinitrotoluene you called it, rolling the word around on your tongue. You tried all those face creams they advertised in the papers but it still wouldn't go away. I told you it wasn't good for you, but you laughed and told me it would wear off once you stopped working there. You were proud of being a Canary Girl, as they called you. You munitionettes all stood out with your yellow skin and the green tinge in your hair. Quite a badge of honour it was. And you had plenty of admirers, despite your funny colour. I think that was one of the reasons you kept at it.

And then I got the measles. Lucky me, eh? I kept thinking you would come and visit, but you didn't. I thought maybe now you weren't working at the Belvidere any more, you weren't allowed in. But you knew the hole in the wall. You could have sneaked in, just like you sneaked *out* to go to the pub. I was a bit upset. And then, when I was well, they told me. You were such a good worker, and your hands were fine and delicate, and you'd been put in charge of filling the shell casings with powder. You had to put a detonator in the top and then tap it down. On the second day, you tapped too hard and the shell went off. And...well...your luck ran out, didn't it, love?

Anyway, I'd better get back. They'll be missing me on the ward soon. I just popped out to bring some flowers for your grave. I'll stay longer next time. We miss you, love.

Afterword: This story is dedicated to Margaret McGuire, a laundry maid whose record simply states: "Died Jan 1911, Buried Sandymount Cemetery, Belvidere Lair."

Soiled Sheets, Spoiled Lives

Lyn McLaughlin

The person whose story I want to tell is Susan Moffat, a laundress at Belvidere hospital from 1890 until her death in 1914. The voice I am using to tell the story is a supposed conversation between two neighbours meeting over time and gossiping about Susan. Susan Moffat was my great grandmother and, although the story is not hers, it documents some of her trials and tribulations. Had she been born a century later, her life would not have been full of grinding poverty and limited choices. This is all that was on offer to her, but her remarkable legacy is in all of us that followed on from her. It's a legacy of Faith, conquering adversity and generally doing the best you can with the cards you are dealt.

~

Hello, Jeannie, how ye getting oan hen? That man o' yours still working? Aye, aye, good. Here, whit de ye make o' that yin in the toap flat? Aye, Mrs Moffat. Huv ye no heard? Terrible, terrible. That's her man deid, only 32. He wis took no well on the Tuesday and was deid by the Friday. De ye mind she came here just efter they goat merit? Aye, an' then wee Mary joined them no' that much later, if ye get ma meaning, Jeannie. Well, she's goat five wee weans noo and nae man. Here, here, did ye know the first thing she did as soon as her man died – yer no gonny believe this hen – she took the weans oot the school an' put them in the Catholic school! Imagine. Whit's that, hen? Oh aye, whit's she gonny dae aboot work? Well, seems that that Mrs Doyle... aye, wan stair up... has goat her a start

in the laundry at Belvidere. Hard work and long long oors. Maybe that'll pit an end tae her airs an' graces, eh? She's a bit la-de da if ye ask me, hen. Comes fae Edinburgh – nuff said. Aw they smart clothes fur her an' the weans; she'll no huv the wherewithal for that noo. Aye, I know she makes them aw herself, but still. You know I don't wish ill-will tae onybody, Jeannie, but she'll need tae cut her cloth differently noo.

(Fast Forward)

Oh, there ye ur again, Jeannie. Aye, it's been a while since I bumped intae ye. Did ye hear that Mrs Moffat loast wan o' her weans? Aye, Sarah died o' the consumption, wee lamb, god rest her wee soul. Oh aye, she's still working at Belvidere, makes ye wonder whit she's bringing back wi' her fae work. Sure, hen, they've a' soarts o' things in there. Often, there are patients in... eh... oh quinine, naw... quilty, naw, whit de you cry it again?

in or oot. Aye, but they wee germs can find a way oot, you mark ma words.

(Fast Forward)

Here, Jeannie, I wis wonderin' if ye wid dae me a favour, hen, could I take your turn this morning in the washhouse?... Ta, hen, it's such a guid drying day; his simmet an' long johns will be dry in nae time... Whit's that, hen, holiday? Holiday? I've no' had wan o' them since... in fact, I've never hud one o' them in ma life. Oh aye, aye I saw them yesterday; Mrs la-de-da Moffat, her, Mary an' the wean. Lovely wee wean wi' a lovely wee lace pinafore oan... Rothesay. Rothesay... that's where they're awa tae. If I ever get a holiday fur masel, Jeannie, am gonnae go tae Rothesay tae... wherever the hell it is.

(Fast Forward)

Oh, holy God, Jeannie, ur ye still oot an' aboot? Dayin well hen; aye good, good. Did ye hear, that's Mrs Moffat deid? Aye, taken tae the Royal an' never got oot. Aye, aye, 58 she wis. Still working, aye. She wisnae really the same since young Susan died having that wean last month. Thank god the wean was awright. Whit's that, Jeannie? How wid I know whit they cried the wean? Oh sorry, hen, you know? Well spit it oot, wummin. Whit? Whit? Yer kiddin' me? You couldny huv heard that right. Are ye sure? Gertrude!

BLOODY EDINBURGH!

The Diary of a Female Surgeon

Yvonne McFadden

I was inspired by a formal staff photograph of one woman and four men who worked at the Belvidere, taken in 1920. It was listed as 'Dr Archibald Residents Group'. Only one of the group was identifiable, the figure of Dr Archibald in the centre. I wondered why this woman was with these men, what her role was and what it must be like to be a woman, quite possibly a doctor, working in an untraditional role. At that time, three Assistant Surgeons were listed as working at the Belvidere: K. Middlemiss, J. Brown and an A. Routledge. It then emerged that the only 'A. Routledge' on the Medical Directory was Agnes Petrina Routledge. Whether or not this is the woman in the picture remains uncertain. However, it did lead me to discover a young woman starting her career as a doctor in 1918, at the end of the First World War. So one photograph has sent me on a journey to uncover the life of a woman surgeon who worked at the Belvidere. I hope to find out more, possibly what she did during the Second World War. My monologue imagines the kinds of challenges she may have faced being a newly qualified female surgeon at the end of the War in 1918 at the Belvidere Hospital.

~

12th October 1918

Dear Diary,

Up early for rounds, as usual. Mrs M was recovering well after her surgery, though in low spirits over her wee baby. Poor woman. Dr Archibald called a surgeon's meeting mid-morning. He confirmed the rumours. The fever has returned to the city. They are calling it Spanish Flu now. After the outbreak in May, we hoped it would be short-lived but it looks like the poor soldiers have brought it back from the Front. They say the War is nearly at an end. What an awful prospect to have survived the trenches and to then be struck down by disease. The frailty of the human body is with me daily. Medical school, or even Mary's descriptions, could not have prepared me for the intimacy of raw flesh that meets me in the operating room. Dr Archibald was more severe than usual today. He wants to discourage cases from coming into the hospital. It is a most virulent disease and there really is nothing we can do. Most expire too quickly to make it here, anyway. Last week, my friend from university's fiancé went to work in the morning and by that evening he was dead!

I had surgeries all afternoon, then rounds again. Dr Archibald accompanied me. Again, he criticised me and referred to me as 'girl' in front of the nurses. I know I've just graduated, but I have had the same rigorous training as Dr Middlemiss or Dr Brown! The nurses often speak to me directly instead of through sister. They would never dare address the men themselves. I think they doubt my abilities because I'm a woman; they often check my instructions with one of the other male doctors behind my back. Dr Archibald's attitude towards me doesn't help. I get so frustrated. To him I'm a woman who got ahead because of the war, just one of many to fill the places at university. Well, my father was a schoolmaster and he educated his daughters, the same as he would have educated sons – if the poor man had had any!

Two years ago, when my sister Mary became a surgeon, he was so proud. And now I'm a surgeon too – if only the staff here would realise it. There's talk that the women in the factories will lose their jobs when the men return. It seems to me that Dr Archibald doesn't believe I'm here to stay. Or maybe, with the men returning home, he expects me to get married! After working in the puerperal fever pavilion for the past few months, the prospect of carrying and birthing children terrifies me. A natural process, they say! The blood, the pain, the death, and the loss... It affects me more than I show. I guess I'm feeling maudlin tonight because Mrs M died this afternoon. I'll need to do a post-mortem. I believed we'd gotten the entire placenta, but sometimes it's just not enough.

I had a letter from Mary in Cambridge; she is considering staying in England after her doctorate. As ever, she counsels me to be patient. I am lonely, though. I knew it would be hard here at Belvidere. The nurses are a good lot here. Despite doubting whether I am a real surgeon, they are generally kind to me. Perhaps I seem painfully young to them – a lady surgeon at 23 years of age! Although they are less formal with me than the male surgeons, they hold me apart. They share their duties, their breaks and their dormitories; while I am an oddity: a woman in a man's role.

As I look down upon the red rows of building after building, everything here is so contained, so isolated. To halt the spread of disease, we must halt human contact. Even in the short months I have been here, there is a steady stream of servants - many of whom run away. Even Dr Archibald has noted all the new faces. He mused that it must be the danger of working in a fever hospital. I think, eventually, the loneliness drives them away. Like me, they must miss their families and friends, living here day after day. But Mary is right! I have only been here a short time. It is a good residency; the Belvidere is a progressive hospital. I'm here to learn and become a better surgeon! Dr Archibald is a great mentor, really – when he forgets that I'm a woman. I'll settle here eventually.

As I write, a nurse has just heard her sweetheart won't be coming home from the Front. Whether it was the war or this dreadful flu, we will never know. My worries now seem trivial when I think of friends who have not returned from the war. Every day we hope for the news that it is finally over. Oh, the thought of this flu is too dreadful. Enough! I'd best turn in. I have to see to Mrs M in the morning. She was such a lovely woman. I have no idea what those four bairns will do now.

Your friend,
Nan

Unspoken

Kate McNab

I was drawn to this girl's story because she came from my home town, so I could picture her in that environment. Her name was Helen Callander and she was 18 years old when she went to the Belvidere. Although Dumbarton to Glasgow is just a half hour train journey away now, at that time it required 3 separate tram journeys to get there, so it must have seemed like a long way away. I could see from the records that she had two sisters and a brother and that her mother died aged just 52 years. At that time, Helen was two years into her training, so it seemed obvious why she had come home. Helen died aged 76 years, still in Dumbarton, so I don't really know if she ever went back to nursing, I hope that she did.

~

The nurse has just given me a blanket to wrap round myself. It's quite chilly in the ward at night. The night light flickers and the shadows flit across your face. I watch as you drift in and out of consciousness. My Mum. The doctors say that you've had a "stroke", a bleeding in your brain. It's been seven days. Dad comes in to see you after his work; the Argyll Motor Factory is just across the road. I come in later, after everyone at home is settled and fed. I prefer to be here at night, when it's quiet. I wanted to talk to you; I've never really talked to you. I wanted to say that I'm sorry. I don't know what exactly I'm sorry for. The only thing that I ever did to you was leave.

Up until then I was always respectful. There was always an understanding in our house that you were somehow "delicate", not to be upset. You didn't like loud noise, raucous behaviour, raised voices. Certain people were not really welcome at the house more... tolerated. Your sister-in-law, Auntie Isa, she was always laughing, always loud. You thought she was "coarse". I know that you and she haven't really spoken these past two years since I left.

You blame her, in part, for encouraging me to go to Glasgow to train as a nurse, instead of staying here. "There's a fever hospital almost across the road, if that's what you want", you said. But they don't train you to become a proper nurse there. You needed a High School Leaving Certificate with a good grade to be accepted to the Belvidere. The Joint hospital took anyone who lasted the six weeks training! You didn't argue or fight, it was enough that you said no. There was just a silent reproachfulness. We never talked. I just felt that if I told you what I wanted to do with my life, you wouldn't understand. I know different, now. But with my leaving, a line was drawn between us.

Isa had come on the tram with me. I had on a new coat and a smart hat; respectable ladies didn't go out bareheaded. You told me that I would meet a lot of heathens in Glasgow. I had no idea what a heathen was, but I promised to have nothing to do with them if ever I met one, that I would always remember my good upbringing. When we got to the hospital I was nervous; it was very imposing.

There was a group of eight of us. We were shown around the nurses' home and the dining room. A dining room! I said goodbye to Isa; she had to go all the way back on the tram, and I promised to write to you and Dad when I got settled. Then we were shown where our rooms were. A room to myself – I couldn't believe it. A bell rang and we went for afternoon tea, where I had the chance to speak to the other girls. A tall, redheaded girl came to talk to me. She'd heard Isa's voice – who hadn't - and had recognised the accent. She was from Alexandria. We became good friends. I was thrilled to be in a place where my past was unknown to everyone; I'd always lived where everyone knew everyone else, and your business was known by all. I had opened a door to new adventures, new friends, new knowledge.

The first six weeks were a blur. We were measured for uniforms; I don't know why they bothered, they never fitted. We were introduced to the rules and regulations. If I had thought that I'd have freedom to do what I wanted or go where I liked, I was sorely mistaken.We worked from seven in the morning until eight at night. Some days were split shift, when we had some time off in the afternoon, then back on the ward till 9pm. Or night duty, which was from 8pm to 7am.

Every nine weeks we were in school for lectures. That was what I really loved: learning. The human body and all of its mysteries. Some of which, I soon realised, were more of a mystery to me than to some of the other girls. In the wards I soon found out why you and your female acquaintances had a low opinion of nurses and had impressed upon me that it was not a profession for "nice" girls. It was demeaning work to be cleaning up after sick people, you said. When I pointed out that that's what you spent a lot of your time doing, you told me that family was different.

It was a new thing for me to be in any way intimate with another person, and so I spent a great deal of time when I was bathing someone with my eyes averted, until Matron pointed out to me that I couldn't report back to her on a patient's condition if I literally went around with my eyes closed. I soon got over that aspect of my work. It was so good to make a poor soul feel so much better just with a wash and clean bed linen.

I've even learned to cook. Soups, stews, fish, puddings. Good, nutritious food to build them up for going home. God knows, some of them don't have much to go home to. I've not had many deaths to deal with, but there have been some. The children are the worst. Despite all of this; the hard work, long hours, the loss of someone with whom you'd become close, I've loved my time at the Belvidere. I've made good friends, learned to play tennis, there have been long chats in each other's rooms talking about the future. Not me, though. I've never been a sharer. I wish I could. I've always felt like an outsider, looking into other people's rooms. I've loved going out into the quiet air in the morning and going towards the wards and my heart just soars. I feel worthwhile, like the Belvidere is where I should be.Yet here I am, home again. And it doesn't look like I'll be going back. I'm needed here, aren't I?

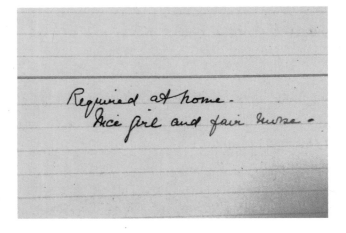

Required at home.
Nice girl and fair nurse.

Tonight, as I sit by your bedside stroking your hand, at last I remember. The anger I felt has subsided. I remember the porridge on the table in the morning, you seeing us off to school, pieces made to eat at dinner time. I remember lying in bed listening to the treadle of the sewing machine as you made shirts,

dresses, underwear, coats. We were always well
dressed. I remember when I opened my suitcase
after Isa had gone, that first day at the Belvidere.
There was newly made underwear, a blouse and
skirt, prettier than the usual.

You'd only spoken to say "mind yourself" when I left,
and not a great deal more on the infrequent Sundays
when I managed to come home in the past two years.
This morning I was putting clothes away in the lobby
press and I found a tin, up beside the washing soap.
In it were receipts and your marriage lines and our
Gerry's birth certificate. There was also a notebook.
It had had a pretty cover at one time but was stained
and faded now. In it were the hopes and dreams of
a young girl; a girl who had been a good scholar and
longed to become a teacher.

And then I knew. When you opened your eyes I
wanted to tell you that I knew, that I understood,
but I just said "I'm sorry". And you nodded and said,
"me too".

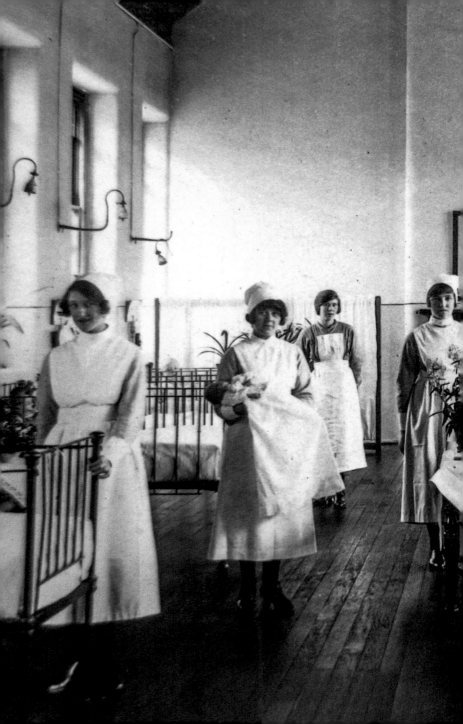